MEET THE TRUCKS

Phidal

Use this page to store your stickers

Warning: Heavy Trucks Ahead!

Match the stickers of the heavy trucks with their shadows.

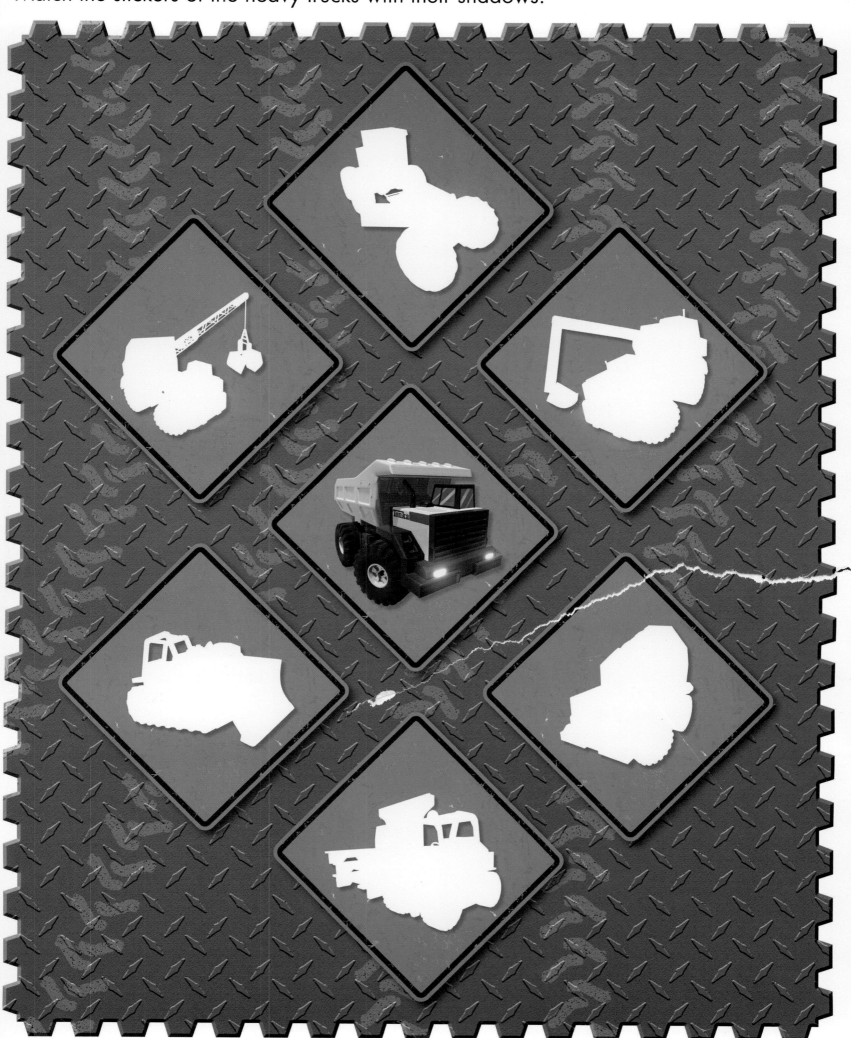

Meet the Fleet

Meet a whole fleet of tough Tonka trucks with your stickers.

TOUGHEST MIGHTY

BIG RIG

MIGHTY DUMP

TOUGH ROLLER

TOUGH QUARRY DUMP

TOUGH FORKLIFT

MIGHTY CEMENT MIXER

MIGHTY CRANE

TOUGH GRADER

TOUGH BULLDOZER

MIGHTY BACKHOE

MIGHTY FRONT LOADER

Downtown Warehouse

Bring this warehouse scene to life with your stickers.

3

4 5

6 11

Big Haul

Match your stickers to the right Big Rig trailer.

Missing Pieces
Find the sticker that completes each truck.

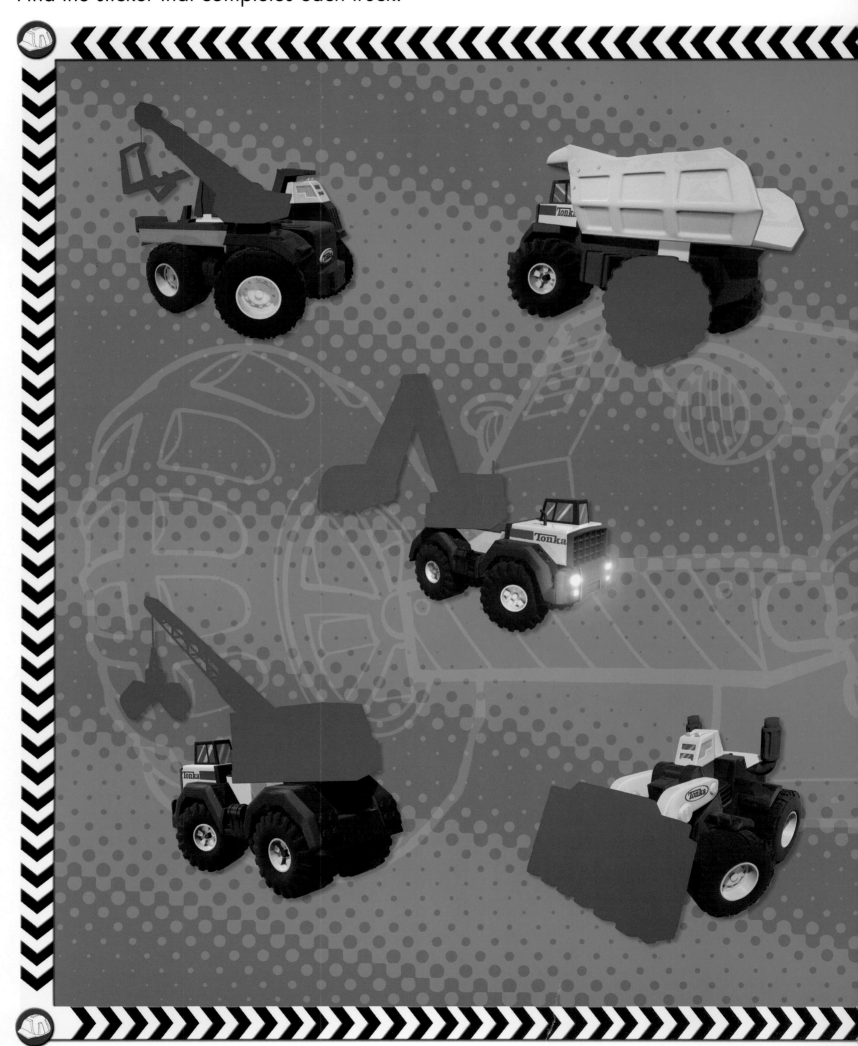

The New School

Use your truck stickers to help build a new school.

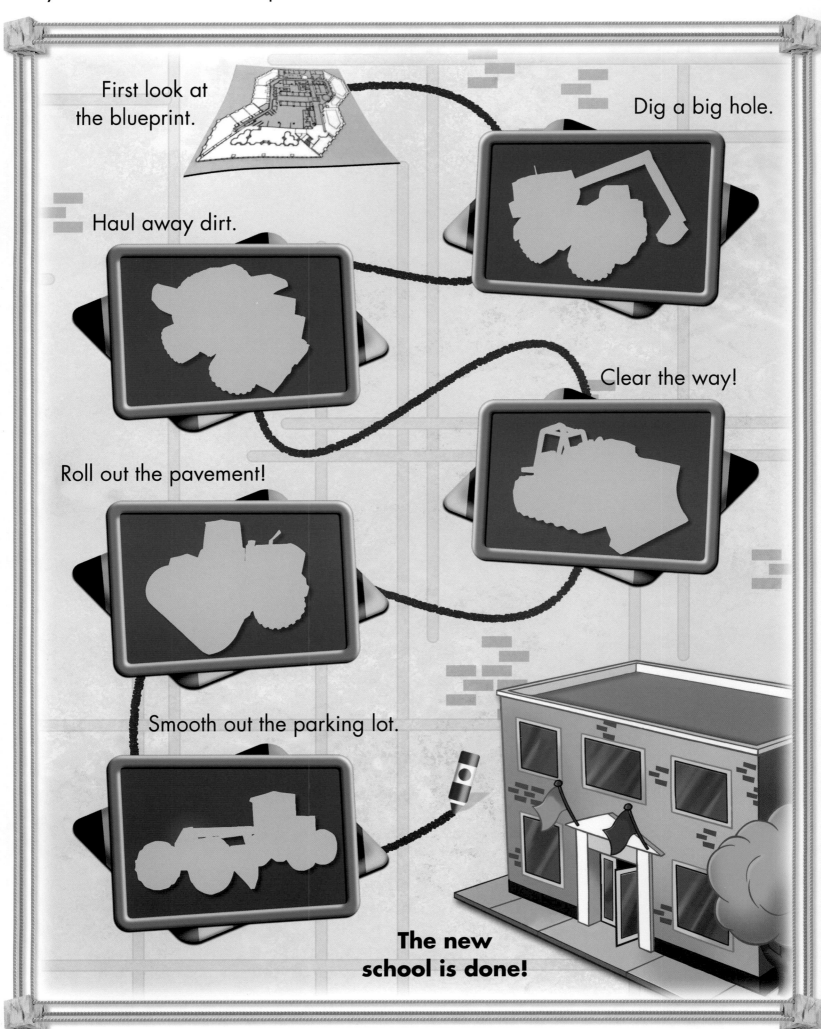

First look at the blueprint.

Dig a big hole.

Haul away dirt.

Clear the way!

Roll out the pavement!

Smooth out the parking lot.

The new school is done!

TRUCKS CAN MOVE!

Phidal

Use this page to store your stickers

Color Code

Match the trucks to their loads by following the colored paths.

Coming Through!

Help build a mountain tunnel with your stickers.

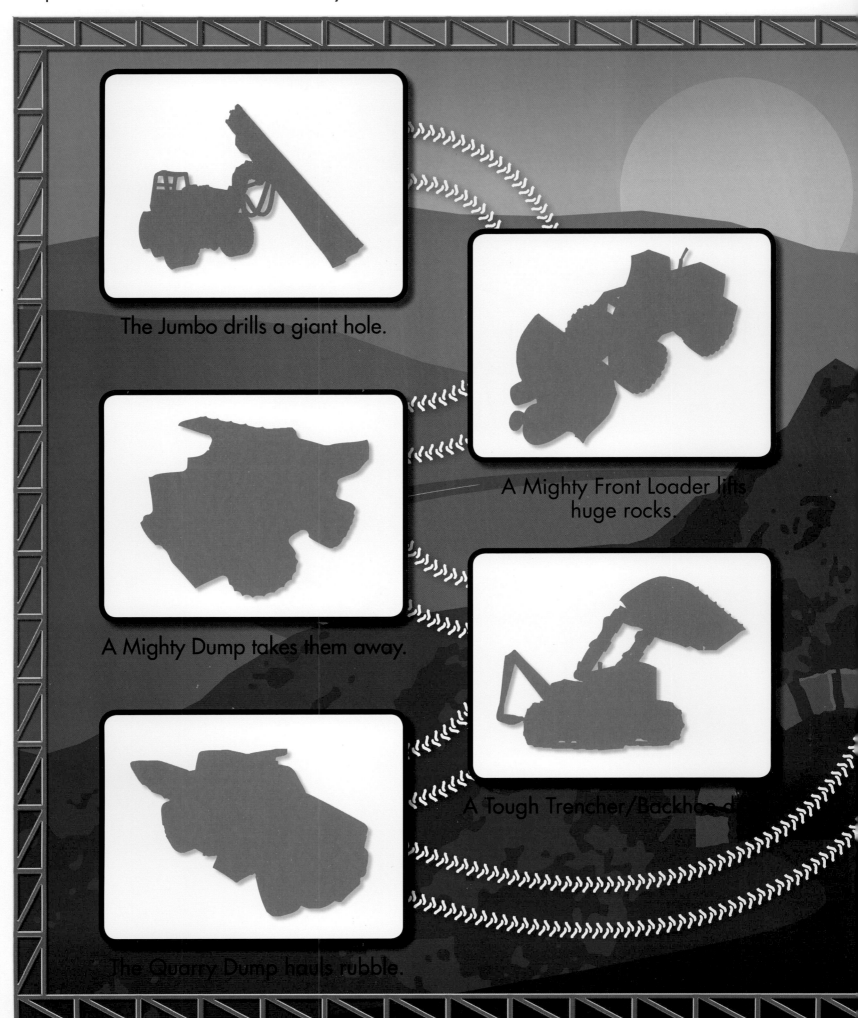

The Jumbo drills a giant hole.

A Mighty Front Loader lifts huge rocks.

A Mighty Dump takes them away.

A Tough Trencher/Backhoe d

The Quarry Dump hauls rubble.

A Tough Grader helps smooth it out.

A Tough Road Roller presses down the pavement.

A helicopter lowers cement blocks.

A Tough Forklift helps deliver them.

Beep, beep! The tunnel is ready.

Construction Site

Use your stickers to show the trucks hard at work.

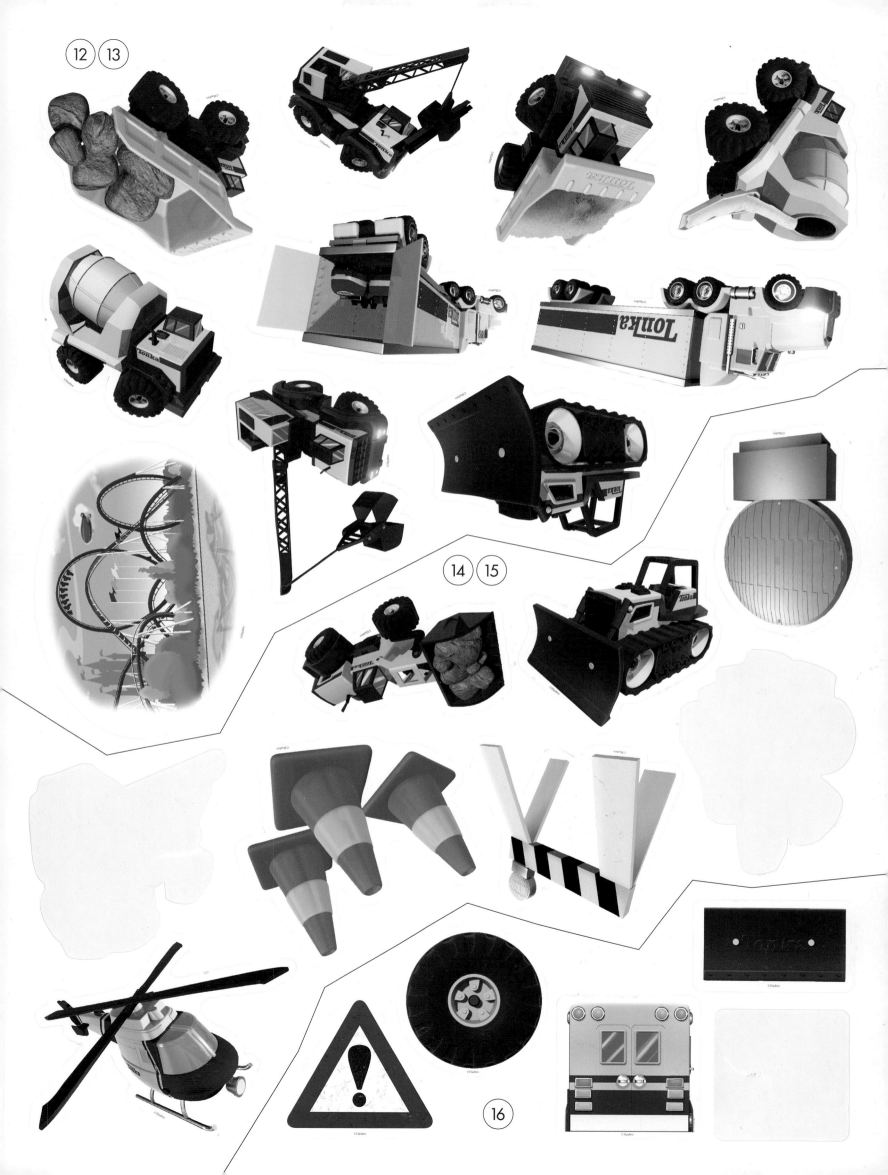

Loop-de-Loop!

Match your truck stickers to the tasks they perform to help build a new roller coaster park.

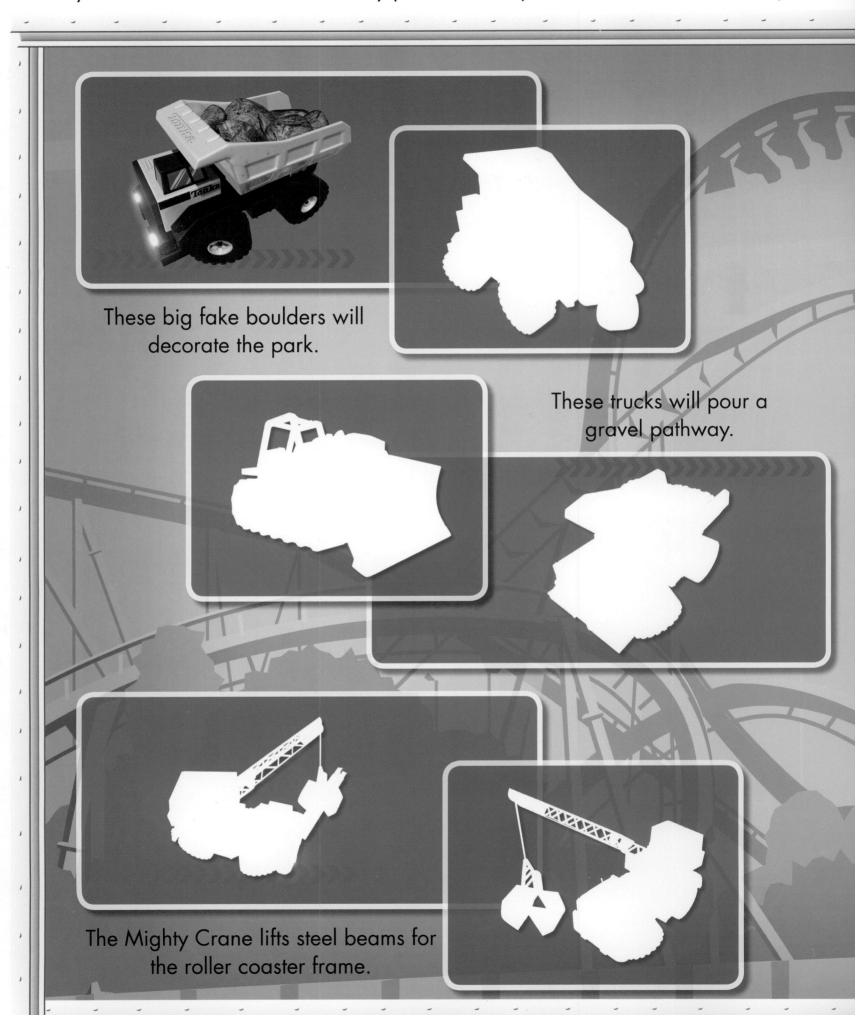

These big fake boulders will decorate the park.

These trucks will pour a gravel pathway.

The Mighty Crane lifts steel beams for the roller coaster frame.

The Mighty Cement Mixer pours a concrete walkway.

The Big Rig delivers the roller coaster cars.

Let's go for a ride!

Mudslide!

The road is blocked with rocks and mud! Use your stickers to help clear the way.

A Mighty Crane picks up debris.

A Mighty Dump hauls it away.

A Mighty Front Loader helps, too.

A Tough Bulldozer pushes away the dirt.

5

Orange traffic cones outline the danger zone.

6

Barricades block off the area.

7

A Rescue Helicopter is on standby.

8

Orange lights cut through the darkness.

Shapes

Match your stickers to the shapes.

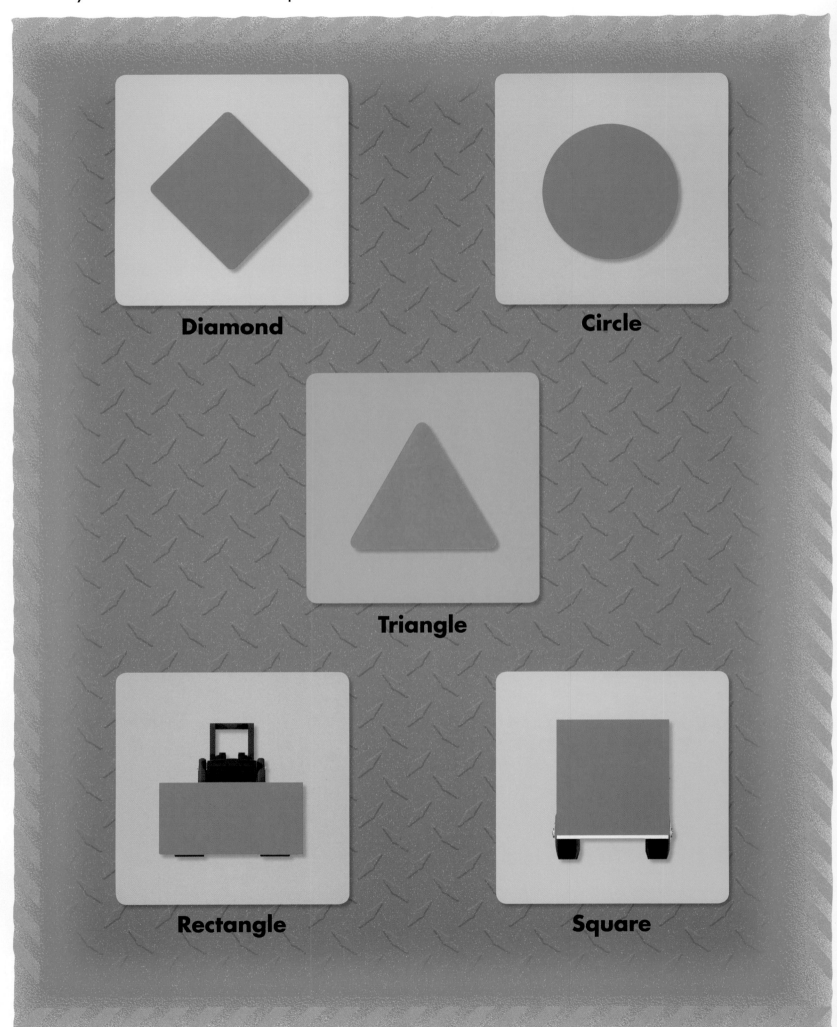

Diamond

Circle

Triangle

Rectangle

Square

BUSY TRUCKS

Phidal

Use this page to store your stickers

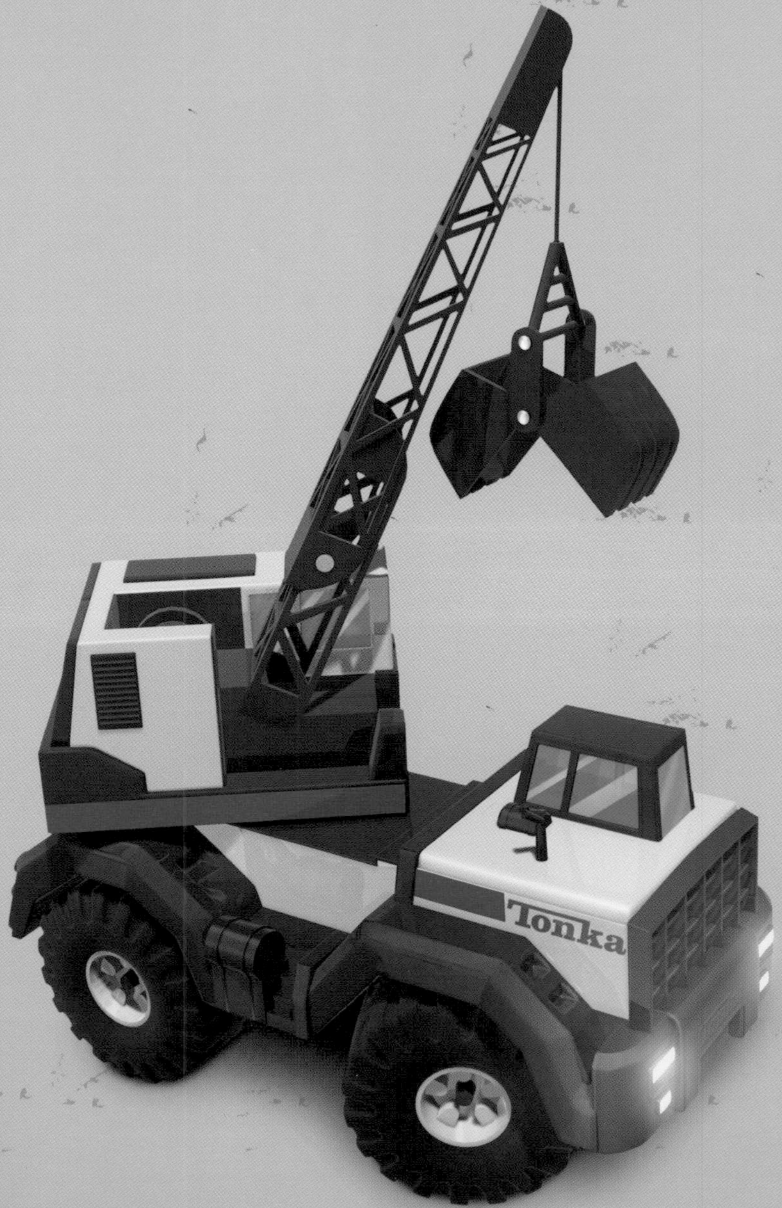

The New House

Use your stickers to make this house ready to move into.

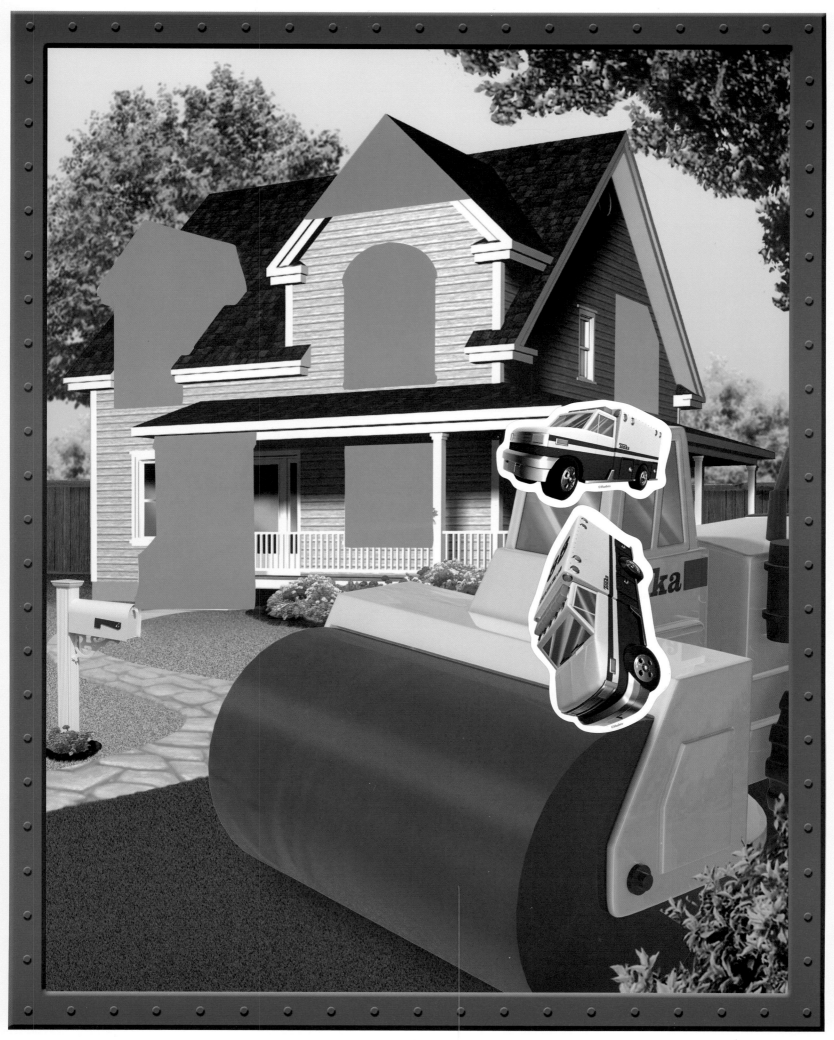

Load It Up

Place each truck sticker next to the load it is carrying.

A Country Road

Decorate the scene with your stickers.

Opposites

Match these pairs of opposites with your stickers.

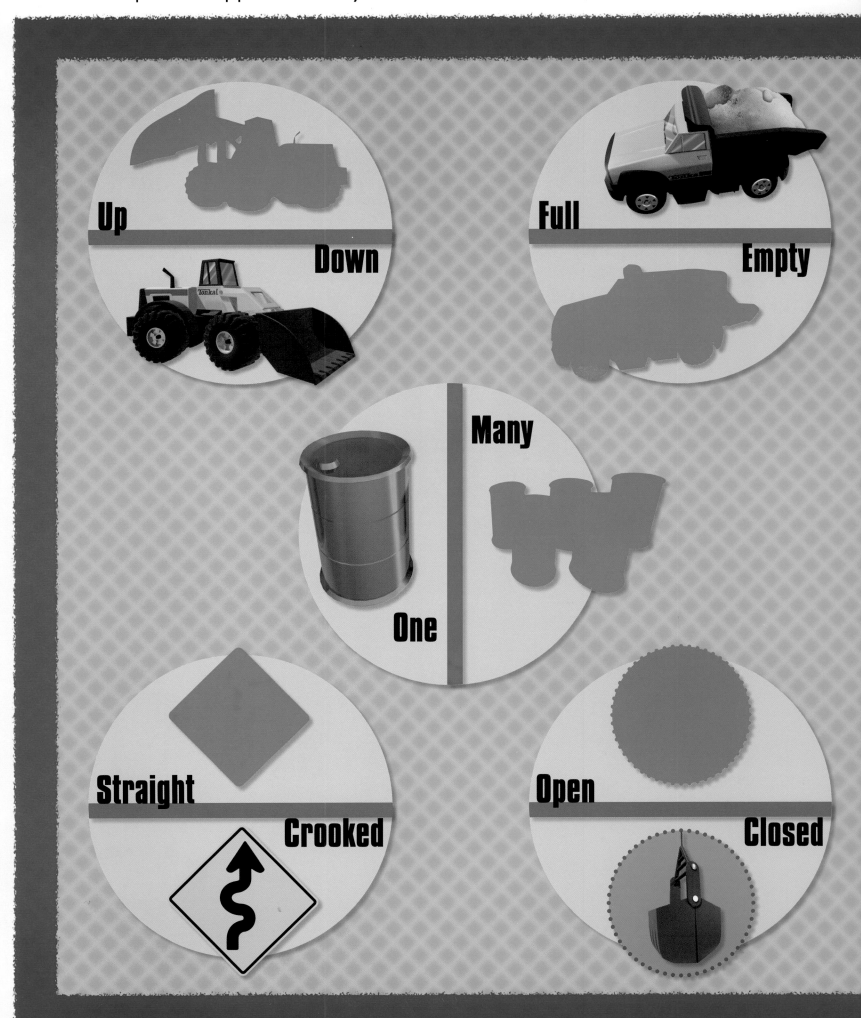

Up

Down

Full

Empty

Many

One

Straight

Crooked

Open

Closed

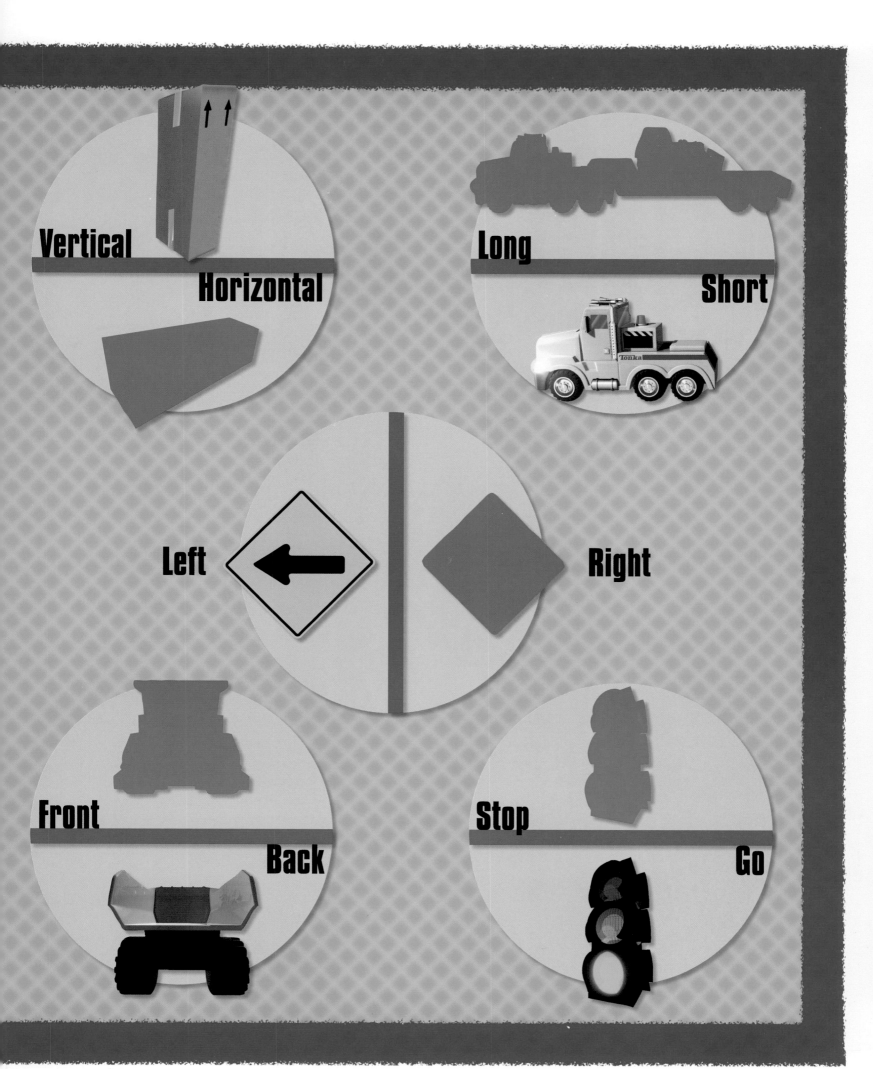

Vertical

Horizontal

Long

Short

Left

Right

Front

Back

Stop

Go

What Is Missing?

Look closely at the first image. Now complete the scene below with your stickers.

Count the Wheels

Sort out the number of wheels from the most to the least.

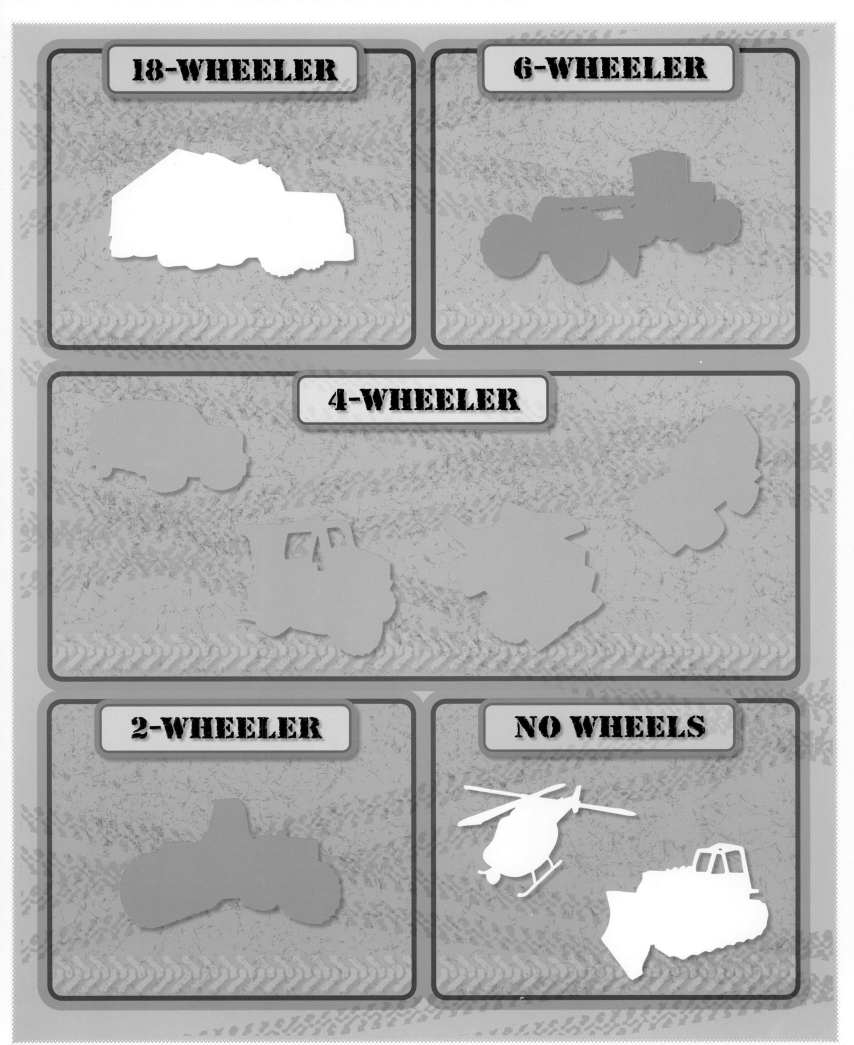

18-WHEELER

6-WHEELER

4-WHEELER

2-WHEELER

NO WHEELS

Puzzle Pieces

Complete the scene with your puzzle-piece stickers.

TRUCKS AROUND TOWN

Phidal

Use this page to store your stickers

. . . .

. . . .

. . . .

. . . .

 **4** **5**

. . . .

Main Street

Help the trucks fix up the downtown street with your stickers.

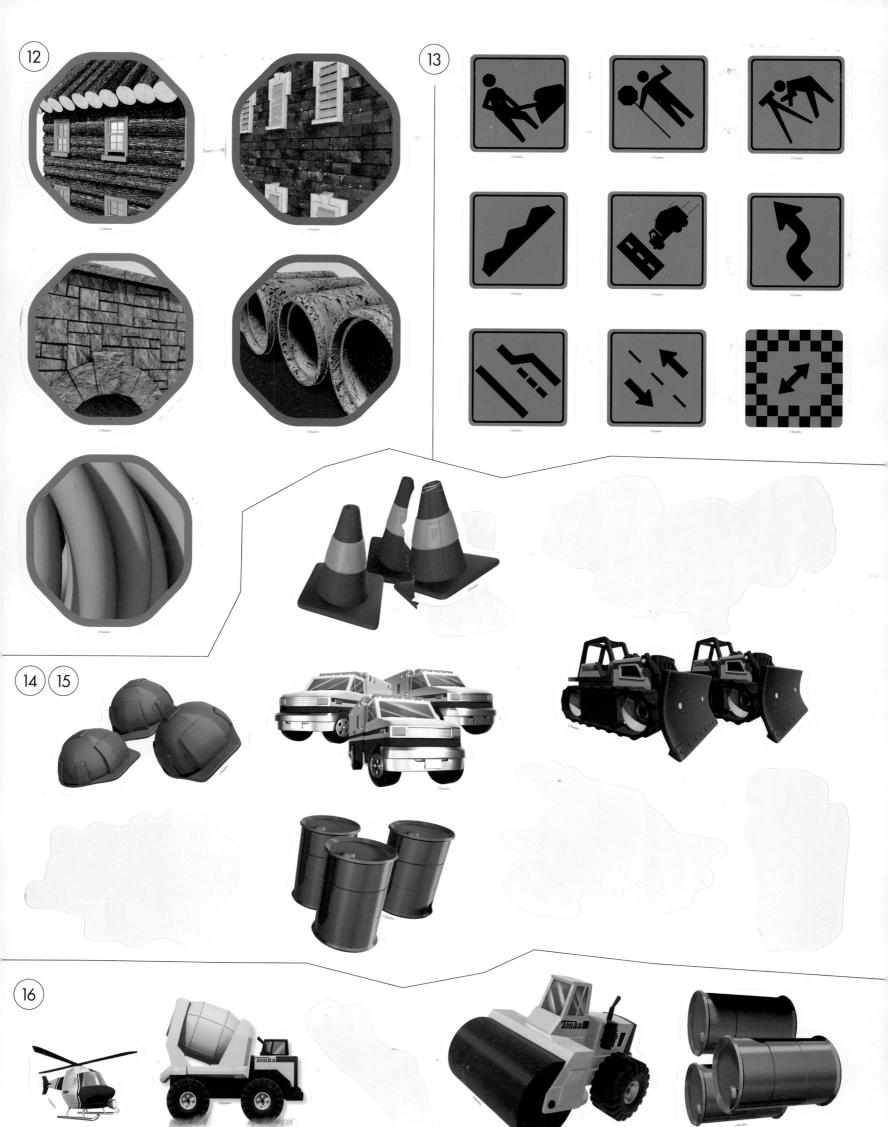

What Is It Made of?

Place your stickers next to the right building materials.

WOOD

BRICKS

STONE

CONCRETE

PLASTIC

A Good Sign

Match your stickers to the construction signs.

Construction work ahead!

Traffic control person ahead!

Survey work ahead!

Rough road ahead!

Trucks enter road ahead!

Curve in the road ahead!

Lane ends ahead!

Two-way traffic ahead!

Sharp turn ahead!

Time to Count!

Use your stickers to count these construction objects from 1 to 10.

Double Take

Look closely at the first image. Now complete the scene below with your stickers.

TERRIFIC TRUCKS

Phidal

Use this page to store your stickers

Rescue Team:

WHAT GOES ON RESCUE MISSIONS?

Construction Crew:

WHAT HELPS BUILD THINGS?

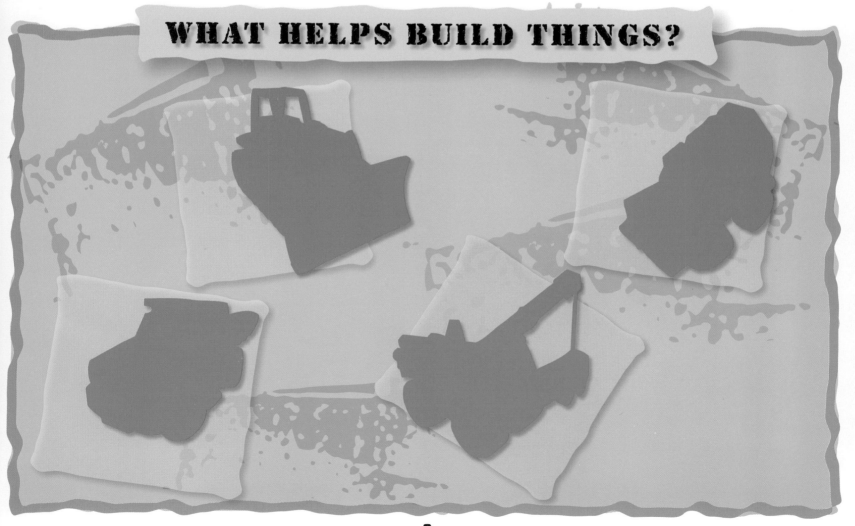

Close-Ups

Match your stickers to the close-up of each vehicle.

Midtown Express

Help the trucks construct the road with your stickers.

6 11

14 15

16

23

Time to Add

Use your stickers to help solve the problems below.

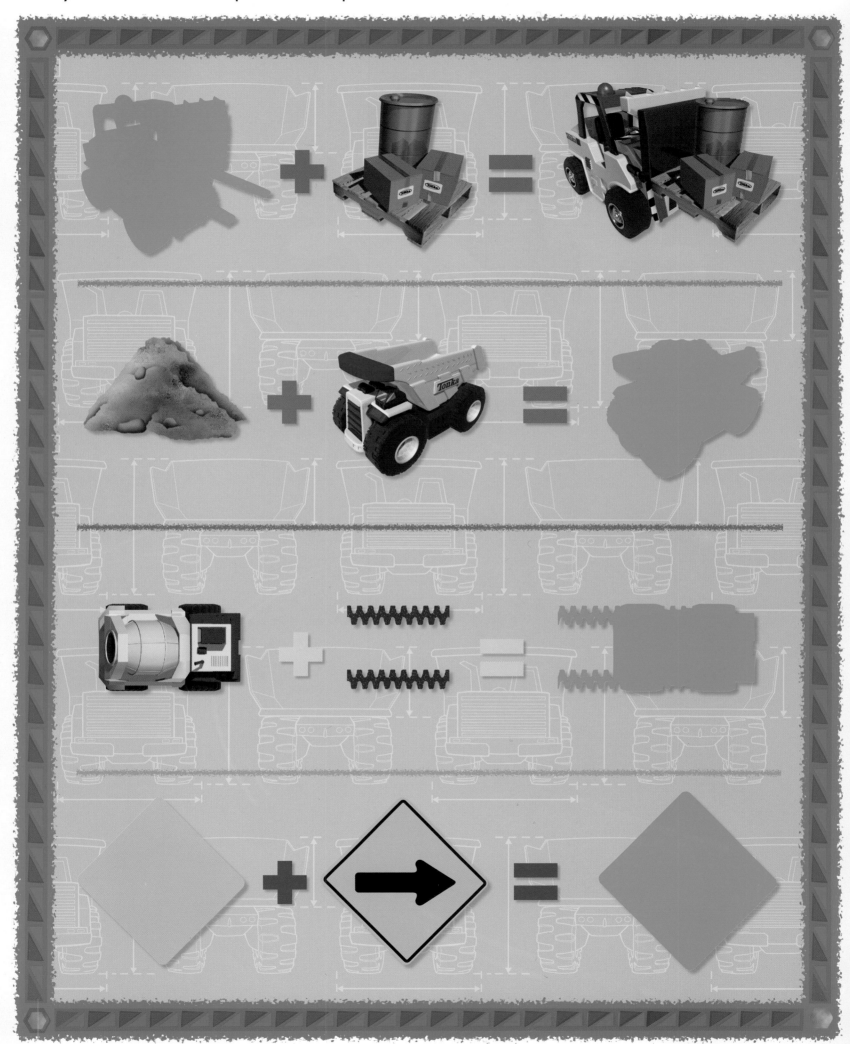

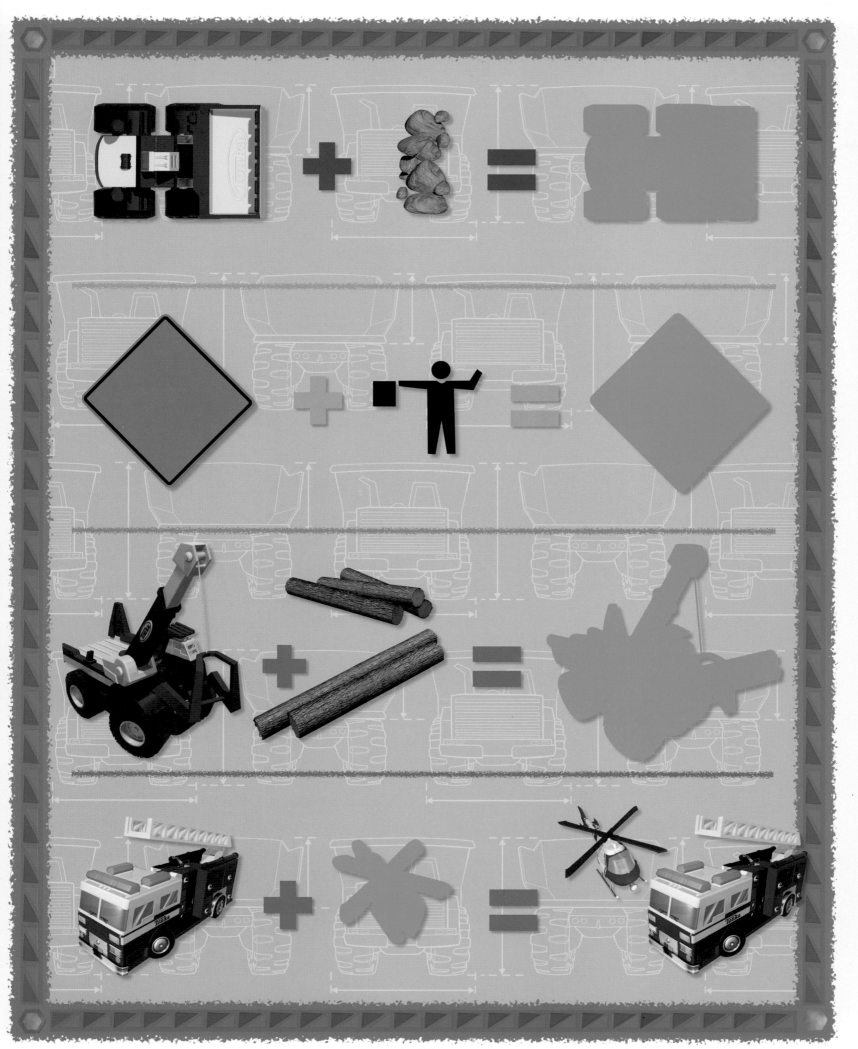

What Does It Do?

Match your stickers to the different actions.

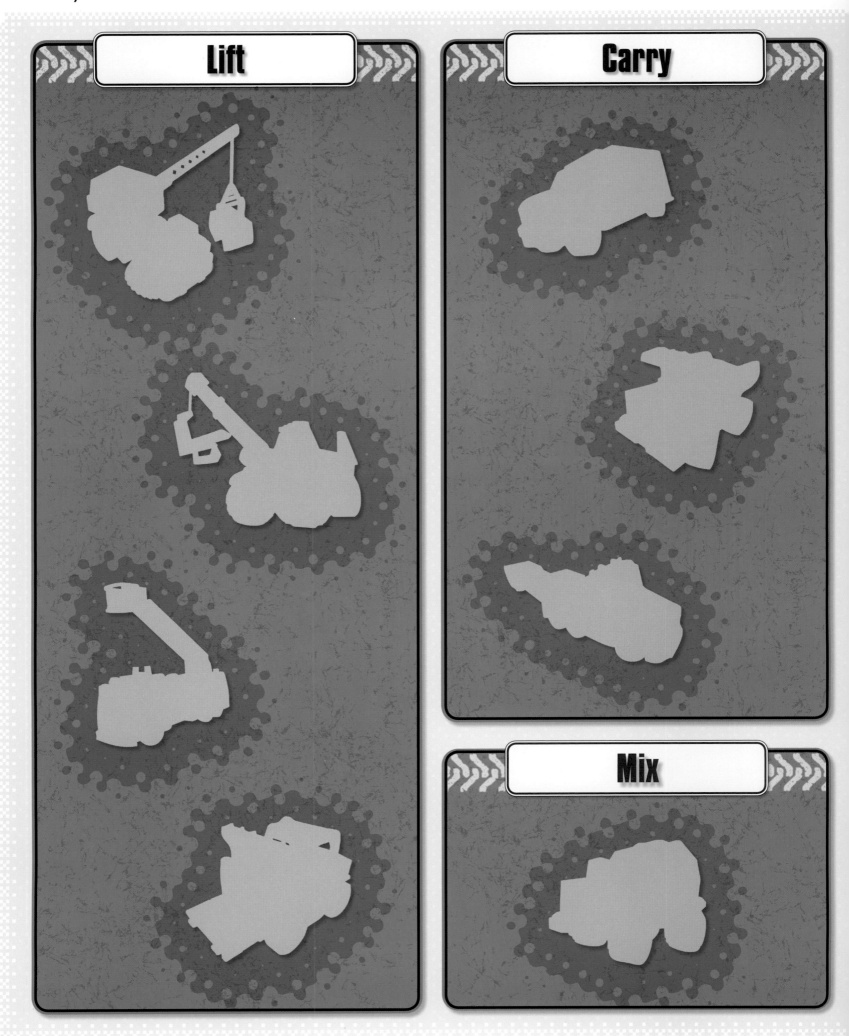

Lift

Carry

Mix

Lift

Carry

14

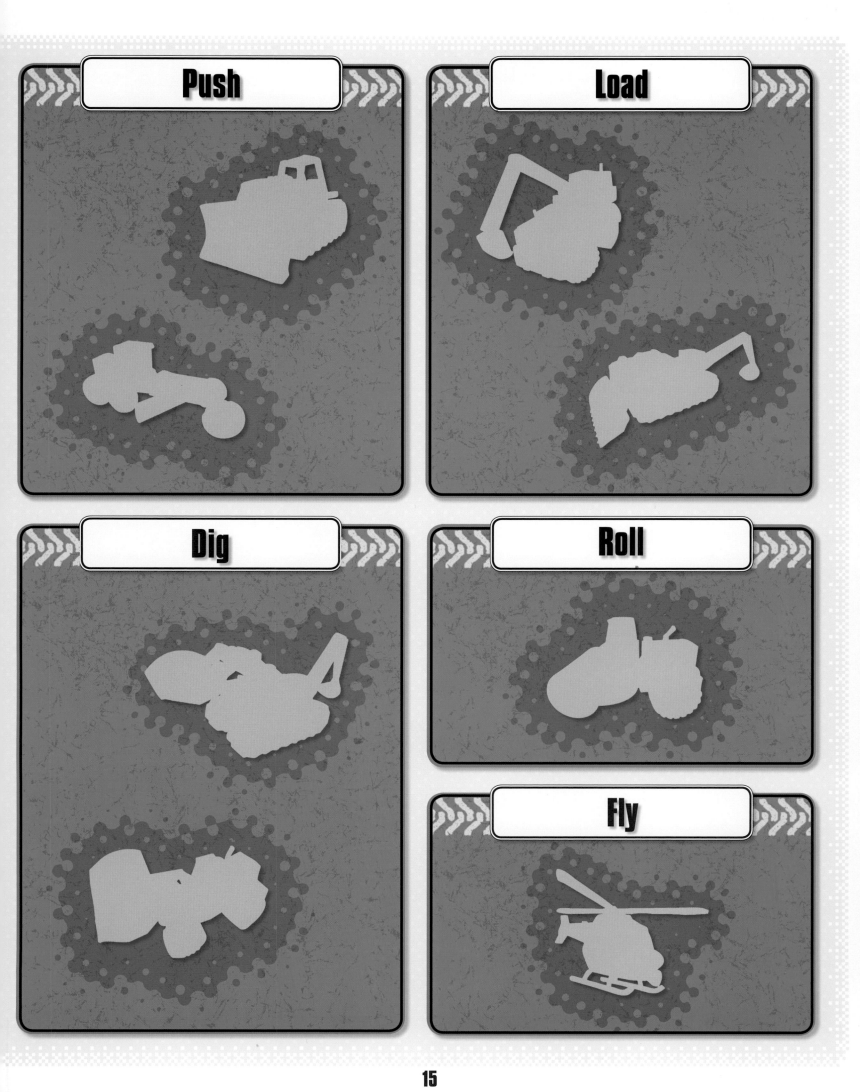

Push

Load

Dig

Roll

Fly

Push

At the Construction Site
What else do you see on a construction site, besides trucks?

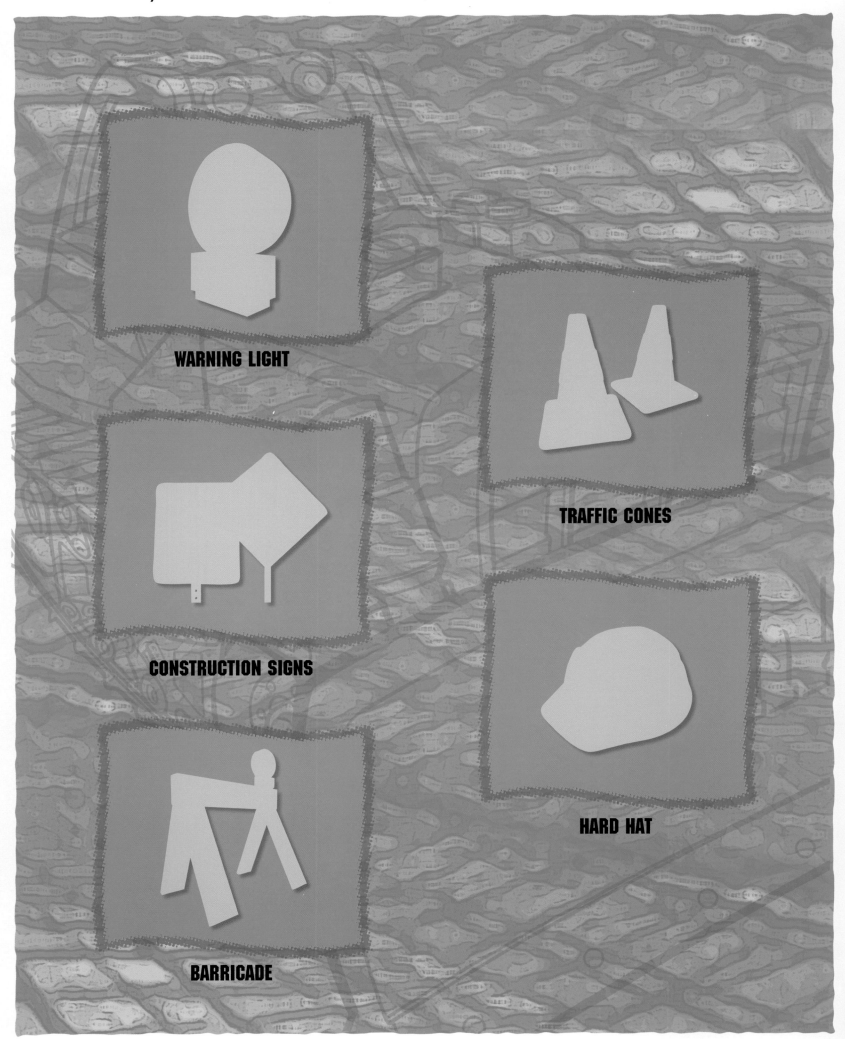

WARNING LIGHT

TRAFFIC CONES

CONSTRUCTION SIGNS

HARD HAT

BARRICADE

TRUCKS AT WORK

Phidal

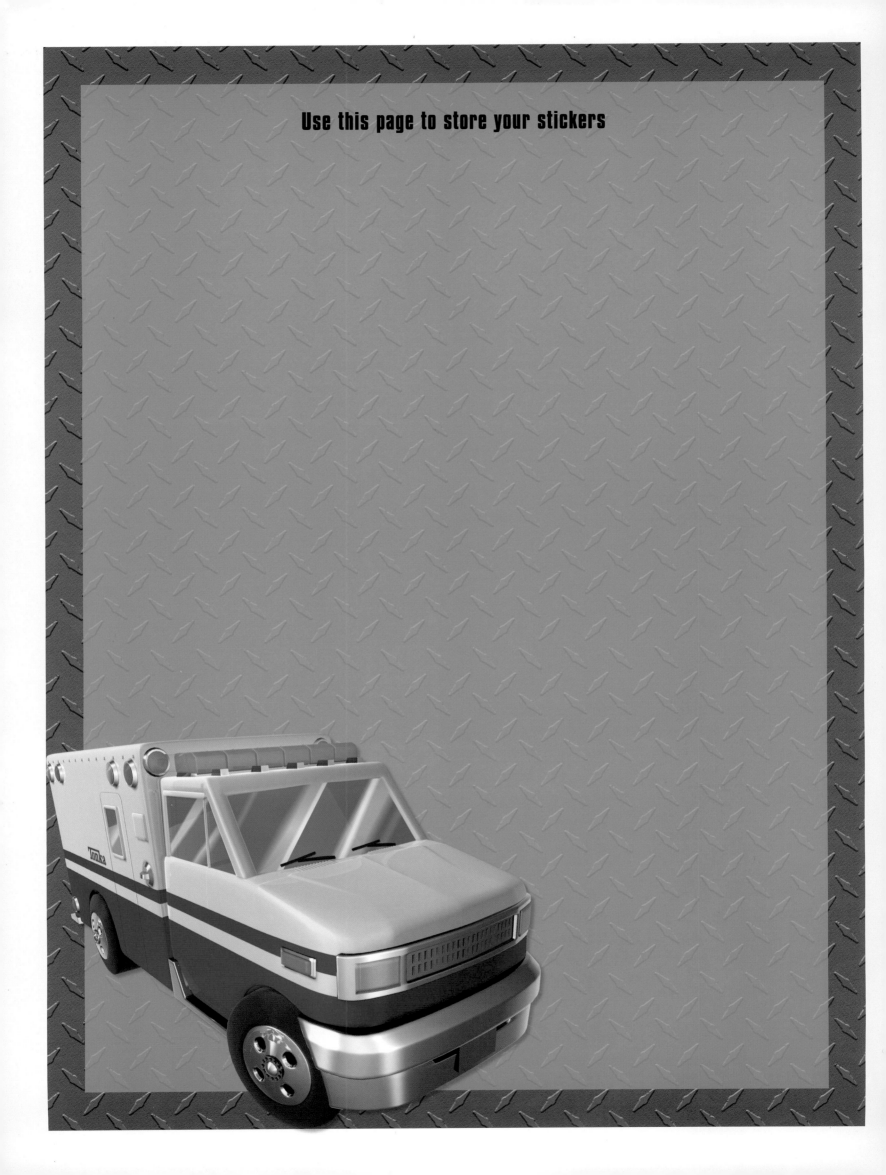

Use this page to store your stickers

Piling Up

Place your stickers next to the matching numbers.

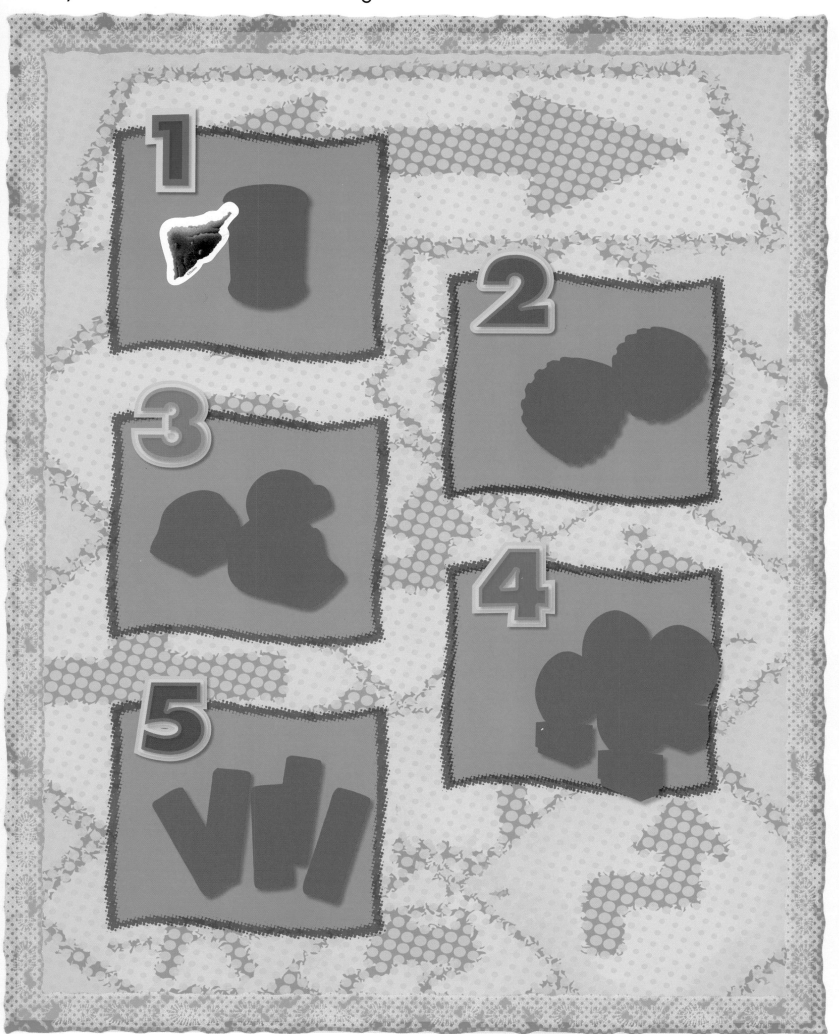

Diamond Mine

Use your stickers to help the trucks dig for diamonds.

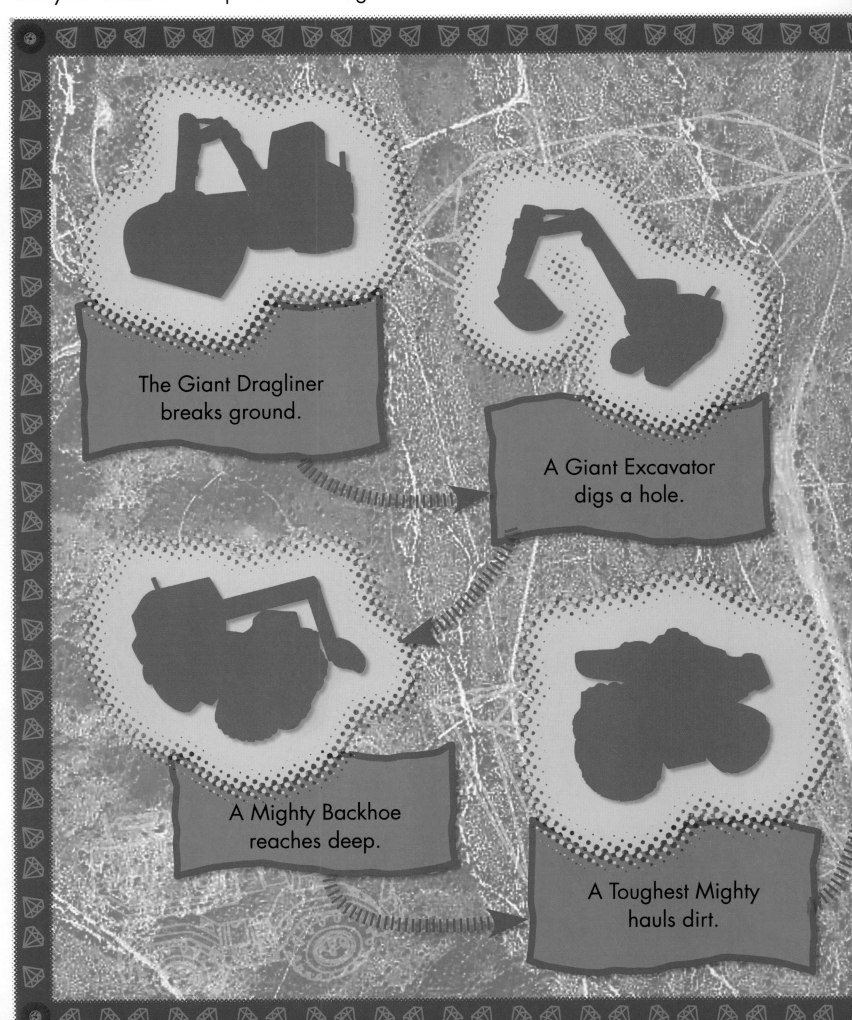

The Giant Dragliner breaks ground.

A Giant Excavator digs a hole.

A Mighty Backhoe reaches deep.

A Toughest Mighty hauls dirt.

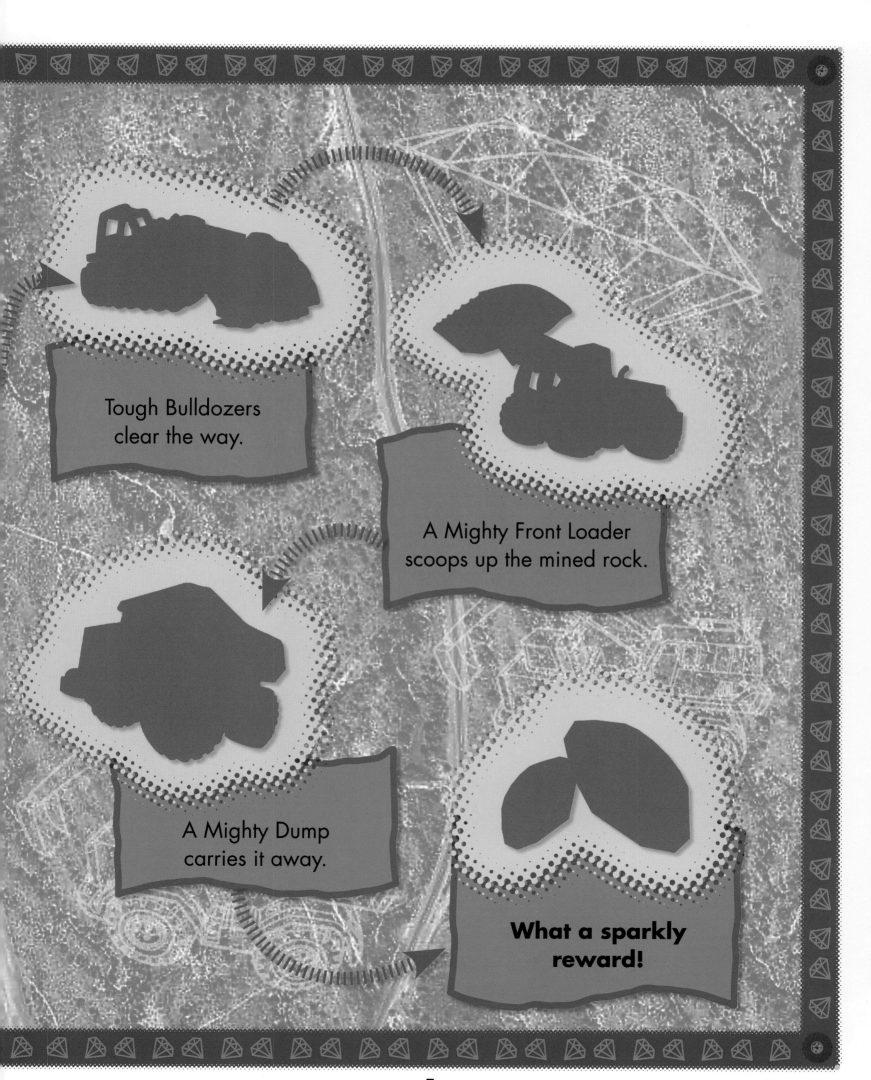

Tough Bulldozers clear the way.

A Mighty Front Loader scoops up the mined rock.

A Mighty Dump carries it away.

What a sparkly reward!

The Old Farm

Put the truck stickers to work to restore the old farm.

To the Factory!

Use your stickers to show how bricks are made.

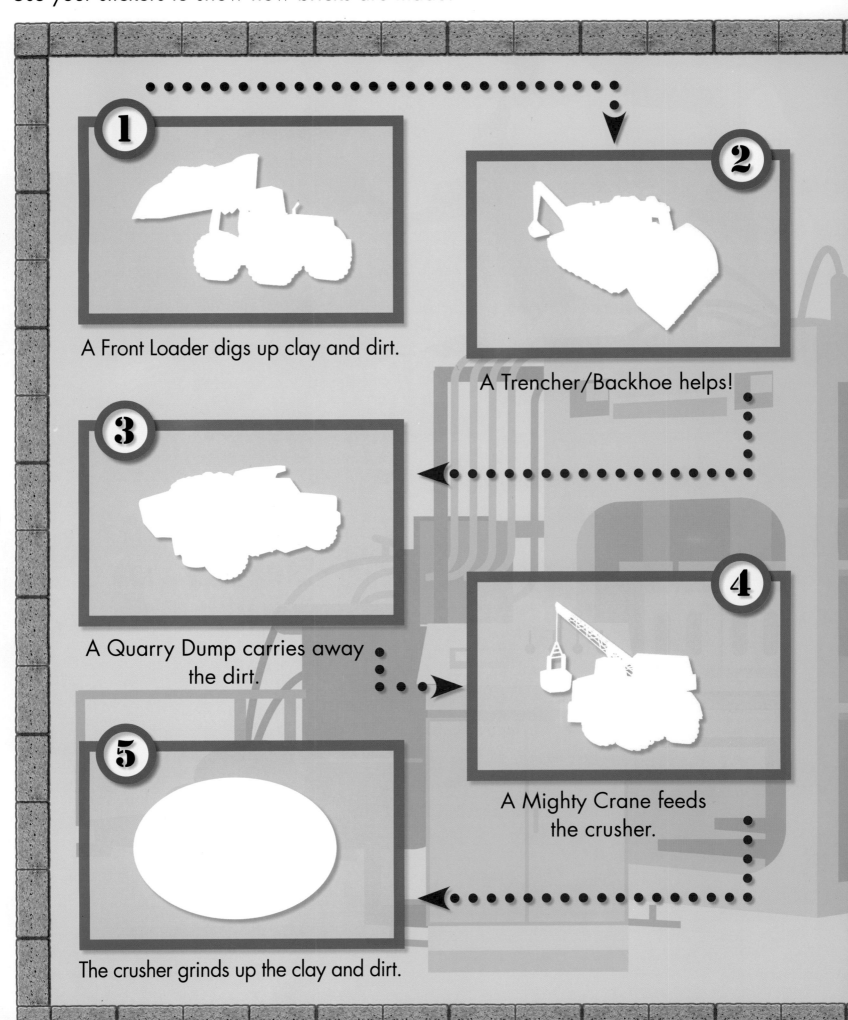

1. A Front Loader digs up clay and dirt.

2. A Trencher/Backhoe helps!

3. A Quarry Dump carries away the dirt.

4. A Mighty Crane feeds the crusher.

5. The crusher grinds up the clay and dirt.

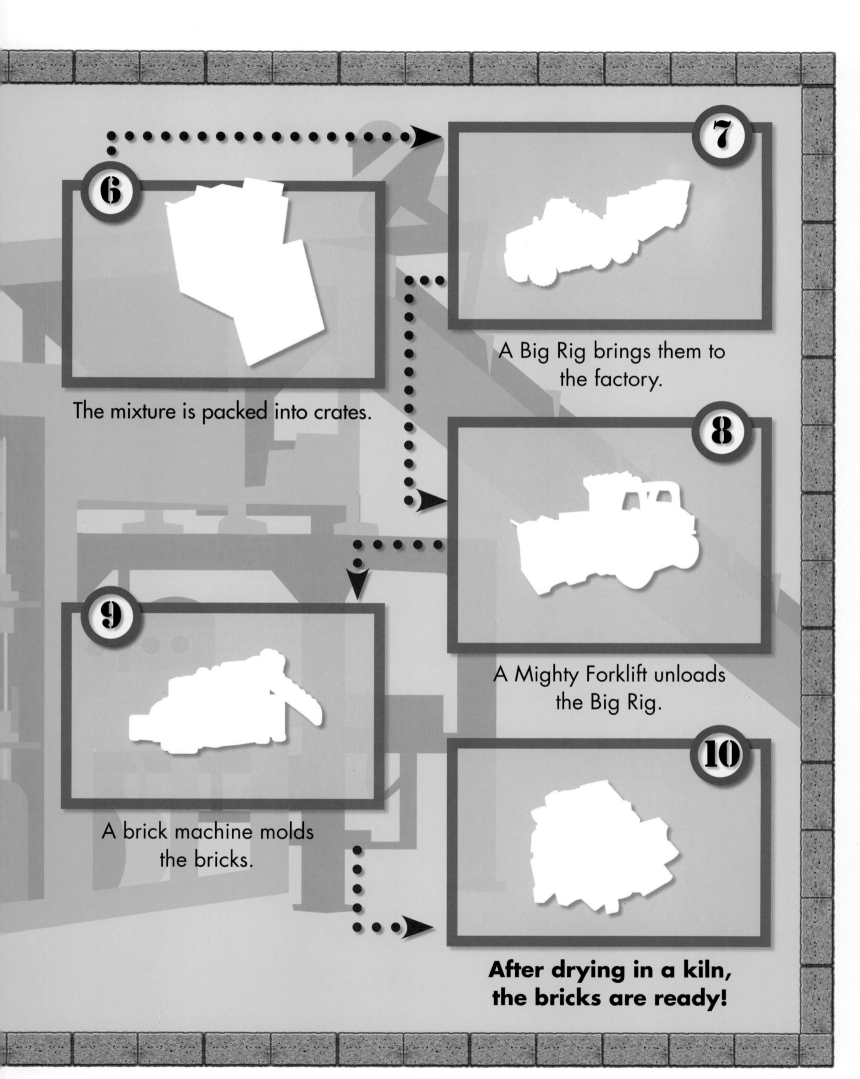

6 The mixture is packed into crates.

7 A Big Rig brings them to the factory.

8 A Mighty Forklift unloads the Big Rig.

9 A brick machine molds the bricks.

10 After drying in a kiln, the bricks are ready!

Follow the Tracks!

Place your tire track stickers next to the matching tires or crawlers.

Fire!

Match your stickers to the tasks as the rescue crew springs into action.

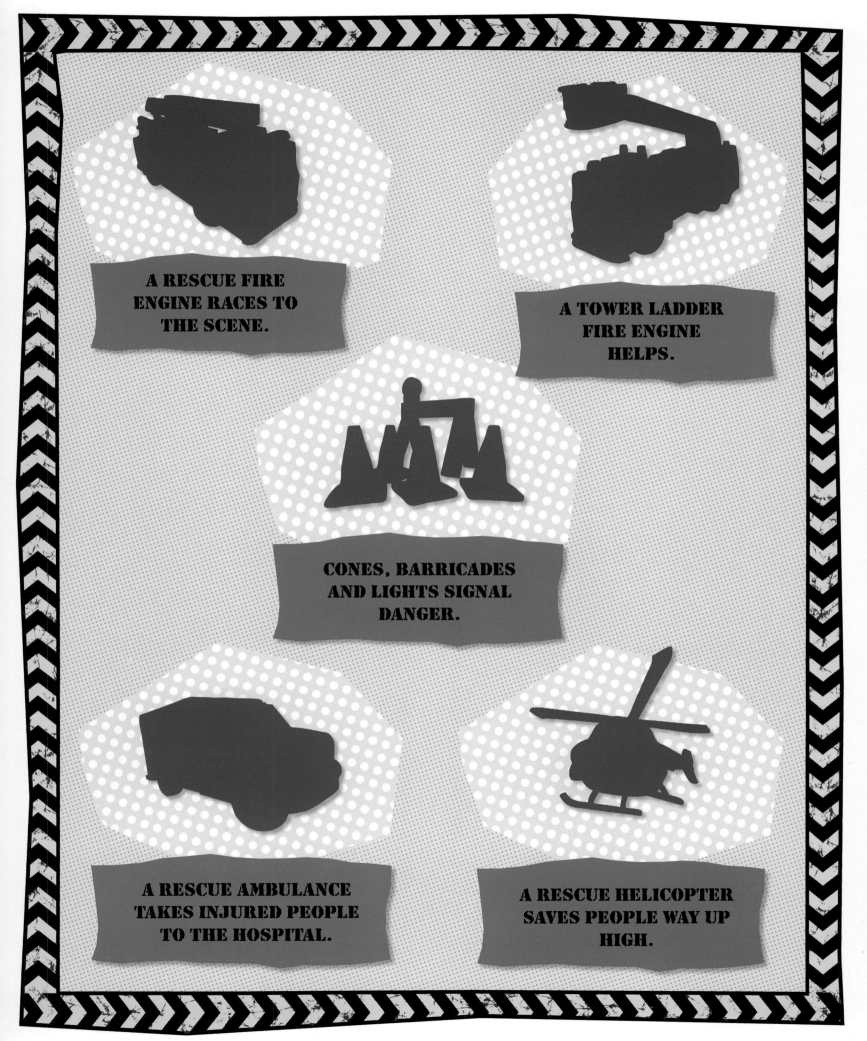

A RESCUE FIRE ENGINE RACES TO THE SCENE.

A TOWER LADDER FIRE ENGINE HELPS.

CONES, BARRICADES AND LIGHTS SIGNAL DANGER.

A RESCUE AMBULANCE TAKES INJURED PEOPLE TO THE HOSPITAL.

A RESCUE HELICOPTER SAVES PEOPLE WAY UP HIGH.

Reach for the Sky!

Use your truck stickers to help build a tall skyscraper.